AGES 6-7
Key Stage 1

Spelling

_ _ide

Bath · New York · Cologne · Melbourne · Delhi
Hong Kong · Shenzhen · Singapore · Amsterdam

Written by Betty Root and Nina Filipek
Educational Consultant: Martin Malcolm
Illustrated by Simon Abbot

This edition published by Parragon Books Ltd in 2015

Parragon Books Ltd
Chartist House
15–17 Trim Street
Bath BA1 1HA, UK
www.parragon.com

ISBN 978-1-4723-5678-9

Printed in China

Helping your child

 Children learn to spell by looking and writing. If your child finds a word difficult, try to follow this pattern:

LOOK at the word; COVER UP the word; WRITE the word; CHECK the word.

Encourage your child to say each letter as it is written.

 Try to find a quiet place to work.

 Stop before your child grows tired and finish the page another time.

 Work through the pages in the right order – they get more difficult as you go on.

 Always give your child lots of encouragement and praise.

 The answers to the activities begin on page 122.

Contents

Contents

Writing names

Write the name of each child next to the correct number.
Remember that names begin with a capital letter.

1. Sarah

2. Jack

3. Eva

4. Tom

5. Lily

6. Josh

1. _____

2. _____

3. _____

4. _____

5. _____

6. _____

Choose one letter to make
each word.

| a | b | c | d | e | f | g | h |

_gg   __nt

_ap   _og

_oat   __en

_ o x   _ ish

Copy the words in order from a to h.

1. __a_____

2. __b_____

3. __c_____

4. _____

5. _____

6. _____

7. _____

8. _____

Look at the picture.
Can you spot something that
begins with each letter?

| i | j | k | l | m | n | o | p | q | r |

Fill in the gaps.

The __ing and __ueen had lots
of pets.

They had a __ion, and a __onkey
and a __ig.

They had an __wl in a __est.

They had a __abbit with big ears.

They fed them all on __elly and
__ce-cream.

Put the words you made in order, from i to r.

1. i _____

2. j _____

3. k _____

4. l _____

5. m _____

6. n _____

7. o _____

8. p _____

9. q _____

10. r _____

Choose one letter to make
each word.

s	t	u	v	w	x	y	z

_ap   _an

_asp   _ellow

_ip   _mbrella

_-ray   _un

Copy the words in order from s to z.

1. s _____

2. t _____

3. u _____

4. _____

5. _____

6. _____

7. _____

8. _____

Animal alphabet

Write a word under each picture. Copy out the words in alphabetical order. Use a dictionary to help you.

a p e

_ _ _ _ _   _ _ _ _ _ _ _ _

Alphabetical order:

1. <u>ape   </u>

2. <u>   </u>

3. <u>   </u>

4. <u>   </u>

5. <u>   </u>

6. <u>   </u>

7. <u>   </u>

8. <u>   </u>

Food alphabet

Write a word under each picture. Copy out the words in alphabetical order. Use a dictionary to help you.

ice-cream

_ _ _ _

_ _ _ _

_ _ _ _ _ _

_ _ _ _ _ _

_ _ _ _ _ _

Alphabetical order:

1. ice-cream _____

2. _____

3. _____

4. _____

5. _____

6. _____

w words

These <u>w</u> words ask questions:

when	what	where
why	who	was

Write them in the questions below. Remember to write a capital letter if the word is at the beginning of a sentence.

1. _____time is it?

2. _____are you going?

3. _____ is your best friend?

4. _____ is your birthday?

5. _____ are you sad?

6. _____ it a good game?

Write the letter <u>a</u> to finish
each word.

b _ t   h _ t

c _ _ t   r _ _ t

Copy each word under the
right picture.

_____   _____

_____   _____

Fill in the missing words.
Choose from the box.

dad	fat	bag	map

**1. I put my books
in a _____ .**

**2. My _____
reads to me.**

**3. I look at a _____
to find the way.**

**4. My dog is _____ .
She eats too much.**

Write the letter <u>e</u> to finish
each word.

b__d   n__t

r__d   w__b

Copy each word under the
right picture.

_____   _____

_____   _____

Fill in the missing words.
Choose from the box.

| ten | fed | pen | wet |

1. I have

_____ toes.

2. I _____
the rabbits.

3. I write with
a _____ .

4. My dog fell in the pond.
He was _____ .

Write the letter i to finish
each word.

p_g   s__x

w_g   p_n

Copy each word under the
right picture.

_____   _____

_____   _____

Fill in the missing words.
Choose from the box.

dig	did	big	lick

I. At the seaside I
_____ in the sand.

2. The cat likes to
_____ its paws.

3. An elephant is a
very _____ animal.

4. Sam _____ not
go to bed early.

Write the letter <u>o</u> to finish
each word.

d_g   f_x

m_p   l_g

Copy each word under the
right picture.

_____   _____

_____   _____

Fill in the missing words.
Choose from the box.

| got | hot | on | top |

1. I _____ a new
bike for my birthday.

2. The bird sat
_____ the fence.

3. The boy ran to the
_____ of the hill.

4. When the sun shines
it is _____ .

Write the letter <u>u</u> to finish each word.

b__s   c__p

d__ck   s__n

Copy each word under the right picture.

_____   _____

_____   _____

Fill in the missing words.
Choose from the box.

| mum | mud | run | hug |

1. We had to

_____ to catch the bus.

2. I _____ my

teddy at bedtime.

3. My _____ takes

me to school.

4. At the farm I got _____

on my shoes.

Write the missing letter to finish each word. Read the words.

d__g   c__p

p__g   b__t

b__d   w__g

c _ t

f _ _ x

w _ _ b

d _ _ ck

n _ _ t

s _ _ n

r _ _ t

b _ _ s

All these words are muddled up. Write them correctly. You can use a dictionary to help you.

	wrong ✗	right ✓
	d e b	_____
	i b b	_____
	g g e	_____
	t c a	_____

	wrong ✗	right ✓
	o y b	_____
	a c r	_____
	e b e	_____
	u b s	_____
	t a b	_____

ch sound

Write <u>ch</u> to make each word.
LOOK at the word. COVER it
up. WRITE it on the line below.
CHECK if you are right!

_ _ air

_ _ _ick

_ _ _erry

 _ _ ildren

 _ _ ocolate

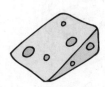 _ _ eese

 _ _ ur _ _

Say the name of each picture and choose <u>ch</u> or <u>ck</u> to finish it. Write the words that end in <u>ch</u> inside the hutch, and the words that end in <u>ck</u> inside the sack.

wat __ __   bri __ __

swit __ __   du __ __

so __ __   wit __ __

hu<u>tch</u>

sa<u>ck</u>

Wordsearch for sh

Look in the blue box for words
that begin or end with <u>sh.</u>
Copy each word next to
the right picture.

s	h	a	r	k	n	b
h	m	f	o	d	e	r
e	d	i	s	h	s	u
e	h	s	r	u	l	s
p	s	h	e	d	o	h

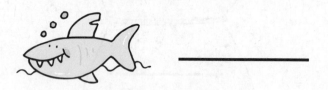 _____

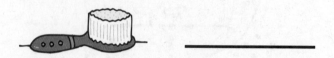 _____

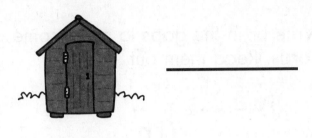 _____

 _____

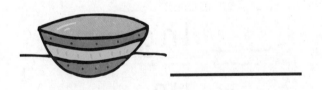 _____

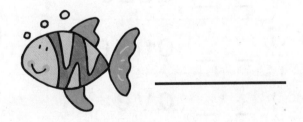 _____

br sound

Write <u>br</u> in the gaps to make some words. Read them out.

_ _	ain
_ _	anch
_ _	oom
_ _	idle
_ _	ook
_ _	ing
_ _	im
_ _	eeze
_ _	onze
_ _	ave

Draw a line to match each word to a picture.

bridge

brown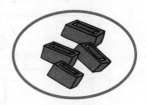

bread

brother

bricks

cr sound

Write <u>cr</u> in the gaps to make some words. Read them out.

_ _y
_ _ash
_ _ew
_ _isp
_ _umb
_ _unch
_ _eak
_ _eam
_ _ate
_ _ocodile

Look at the picture clues.
Write the letters cr in the
correct place in the crossword.

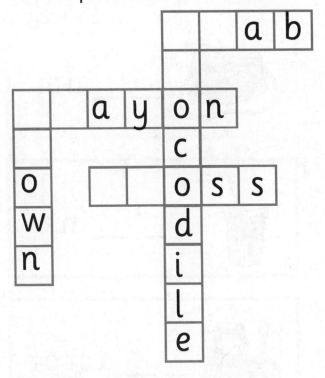

Across   **Down**

dr or tr?

Write <u>dr</u> or <u>tr</u> in the gaps to make some words.

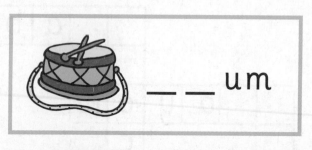 _ _ _ um

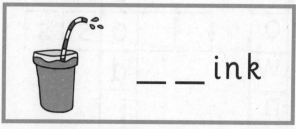 _ _ _ ink

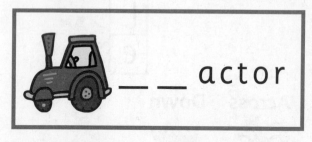 _ _ _ actor

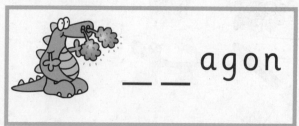 _ _ _ agon

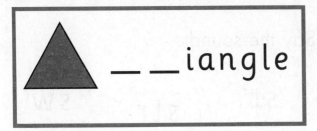

_ _iangle

_ _uck

Cover up the words you wrote.
Write a <u>dr</u> or <u>tr</u> word in each gap.

1. It's green and
   blows out fire. _____

2. You bang on it.

   _____

3. You have it when
   you are thirsty. _____

4. A farmer drives it.

   _____

Sounds: st, str, sp, sl, sw

Say the sounds:

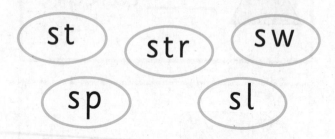

st

str

sw

sp

sl

Say the name of each
picture. Write the sound
to match the picture.

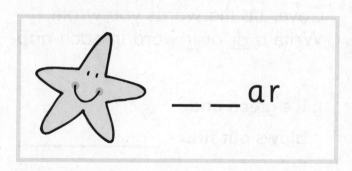

__ __ ar

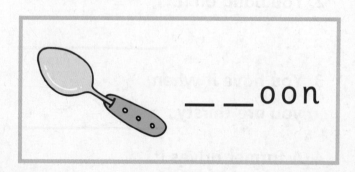

__ __ oon

 _ _ amp

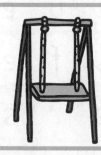 _ _ ing

 _ _ _ awberry

 _ _ ide

Look in the blue box for words that begin with <u>bl</u>, <u>cl</u> or <u>fl</u>. Copy each word next to the right picture.

c	l	c	b	l	u	e
l	f	l	b	l	f	e
f	l	o	w	e	r	s
l	a	c	l	o	u	d
g	g	k	c	h	l	b
z	b	k	b	b	l	l
y	l	b	l	a	c	k

 _____

Write <u>th</u> to make each word.
LOOK at the word. COVER it
up. WRITE it on the line below.
CHECK if you are right!

 _ _ umb

 _ _ rone

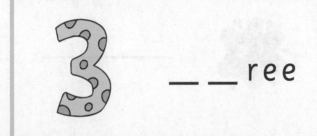 _ _ ree

 __ __istle

 ba__ __

 too__ __brush

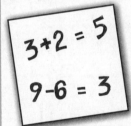 ma__ __s

Say the name of each picture. Spell the word next to each picture.

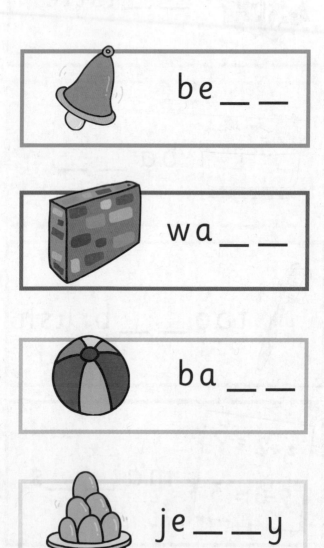

be _ _

wa _ _

ba _ _

je _ _ y

umbre __ __ a

ro __ __ er skate

ye __ __ ow

ba __ __ oons

caterpi __ __ ars

Double letters: dd, rr, tt, ss, zz

Say the name of each picture. Spell the word next to each picture.

bo _ _ le

ke _ _ le

te _ _ y

che _ _ y

 la_ _er

 ca_ _ot

 pi_ _a

 gra_ _

 bu_ _erfly

Say the name of each picture. Spell the word next to each picture.

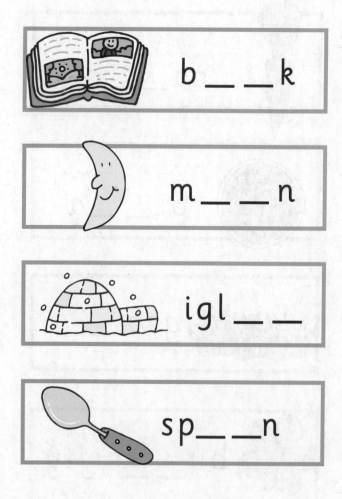

b _ _ k

m _ _ n

igl _ _

sp _ _ n

 ball_ _n

 kangar_ _ _

 d_ _ _r

 t_ _ _th

 h_ _ _k

ow or ou?

Say what is in the picture.
Write <u>ow</u> or <u>ou</u> to make a word.

c _ _

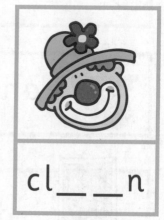

cl_ _ _n

m_ _ _se

h_ _ _se

__ __ l

fl___ers

rainb___

cr___n

wind___

 goat

 pear

 boat

 coat

 feather

Choose a word to fill each gap.

1. I felt sea sick on the

_____ .

2. I saw a _____ on
the farm.

3. I put on my _____ .

4. I can eat a _____ .

5. I found a _____ .

Middle sound: ai

Say what is in the picture.
Spell the word next to it.

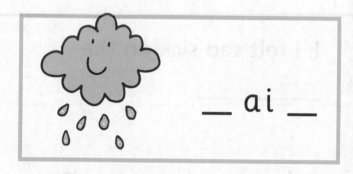

_ a i _

_ _ a i _

a i

_ _   _ _ _ _

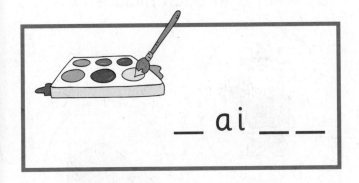

_ ai ___ _

_ ai _

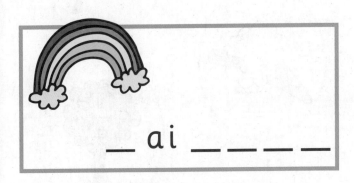

_ ai _ _ _ _

ee or ea?

Say what is in each picture.

Spell the words you said.
Write each word on the
correct list. Check your spellings
in a dictionary.

ee	ea
cheese	

Fill in the missing letters. Choose ai as in snail or ea as in leaf. Write the whole word.

s _ _ t   tr _ _ n

_____   _____

b _ _ k

_____

 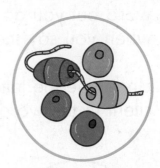

t_ _ l   b_ _ ds

_____   _____

r_ _ n

_____

Silent letters

Some words have silent letters. You see a silent letter in a word but you do not hear it when you say the word.

Underline the letters that are silent in the words below.

knife

guitar

knight

wheel

comb

thumb

wrist

badge

gnome

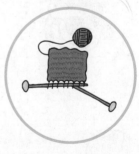

knitting

Rhyming words

Draw lines to join the words that end with the same sounds.

Choose words from this list to complete the rhyme.

out sprout spout shout
rain train again

Incy Wincy Spider climbed up the water _____.

Down came the rain and washed the spider _____.

Out came the sunshine and dried up all the _____.

Now Incy Wincy Spider climbed up the spout _____!

Same sounds

Some words rhyme but have very different spelling patterns.

Write a word under each picture. Draw a line to join the words that rhyme.

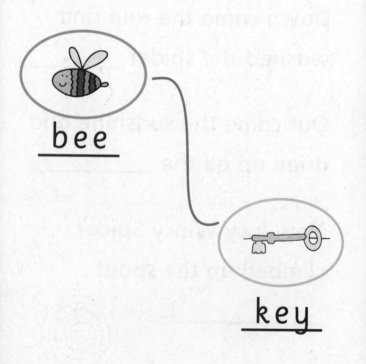

bee

key

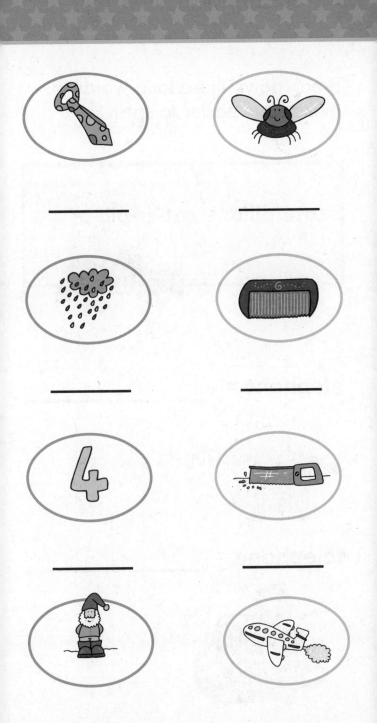

Break down these long words to make them easier to spell.

caterpillar = cat-er-pill-ar

elephant = _____

telephone = _____

magician = _____

policewoman = _____

banana = _____

butterfly = _____

See if you can do this. The first one has been done for you.

Try it!

h–am–mer

hammer

_____

cloud

flower _____

church _____

crown _____

spider _____

Everyday words

Copy the words from the box into the right sentences.

laugh	because	here
once	water	would

1. I _____ like a
new bike.

2. I am staying indoors
_____ it is raining.

3. My sister likes to make me _____ .

4. I _____ went to a football match.

5. I wash with _____ .

6. _____ is my house.

Colours

LOOK at the word. COVER it up.
WRITE it on the line. CHECK if
you are right!

blue _____

green _____

red _____

orange _____

yellow _____

pink _____

 purple _____

 black _____

 white _____

 grey _____

 brown _____

Days of the week

Finish these sentences.

Monday

**On _____ I
go swimming.**

Tuesday

**On_____I
play football.**

Wednesday

**On_____I
feed the ducks.**

On _____
**I help Dad do
the shopping.**

Thursday

On _____
**I go to see
my gran.**

Friday

On _____
I go to a party.

Saturday

On _____
**I help Mum
wash her car.**

Sunday

Compound words

A compound word is made up of two short ones. Write a word under each picture. Join two pictures to make a compound word.

star

fish

Now write your new words.

starfish

_____

_____

_____

_____

Write a word under each picture. Join two pictures to make a compound word.

_____   _____

_____   _____

_____   _____

_____   _____

Now write your new words.

_____

_____

_____

_____

Patterns in words

Read the word above each row. Circle the pictures that end with the same letters.

p<u>ick</u>

r<u>est</u>

l<u>ate</u>

thi<u>stle</u>

si<u>ght</u>

<u>r</u>i<u>ng</u>

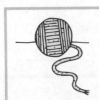

Hidden words

Find one little word hiding in each big word. Write the little words in the spaces.

1. balloon	___
2. supper	___
3. something	___
4. mother	___
5. horse	___
6. kitten	___
7. dinosaur	___
8. winter	___

Write sentences using four of the words that you found.

1. _____

_____

2. _____

_____

3. _____

_____

4. _____

_____

Definitions

Join each sentence to the right picture. Copy the word into the space by the picture.

1. A banana is a yellow fruit. You peel off its skin.

2. A brush is used for painting.

3. A butterfly is an insect with pretty wings.

4. A panda is a big black and white animal.

5. You wear a sock on your foot.

6. A frog lives by water. It can jump a long way.

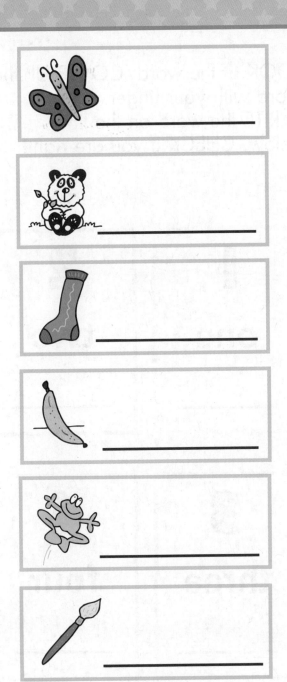

LOOK at the word. COVER UP the word with your finger.
WRITE the word on the line below. CHECK if you are right!

1	2
one	**two**
_____	_____

3	4
three	**four**
_____	_____

5	6
five	six
_____	_____

7	8
seven	eight
_____	_____

9	10
nine	ten
_____	_____

LOOK at the word. COVER UP the word with your finger. WRITE the word on the line below. CHECK if you are right!

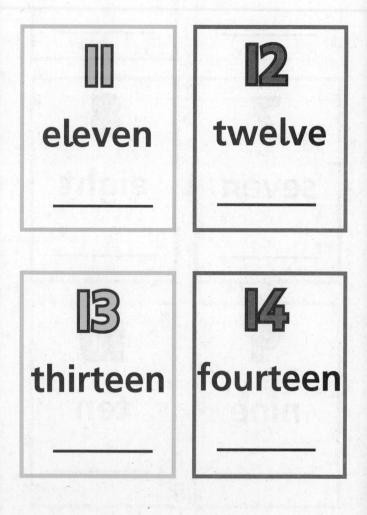

11 eleven

_____

12 twelve

_____

13 thirteen

_____

14 fourteen

_____

fifteen

_____

sixteen

_____

seventeen

_____

eighteen

_____

19

nineteen

_____

20

twenty

_____

Magic e

Add the letter e to a short word and magic happens.
The letter in the middle of the word changes its sound and the word changes its meaning.

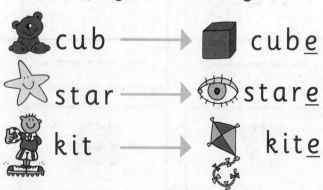

cub ⟶ cub<u>e</u>

star ⟶ stare

kit ⟶ kit<u>e</u>

Use magic e on these words.

cap ⟶ _ _ _ _

hat ⟶ _ _ _ _

her ⟶ _ _ _ _

bit ⟶ _ _ _ _

not ⟶ _ _ _ _

tub ⟶ _ _ _ _

The middles are missing from these words. Put the same missing letter in each pair of words, like this:

rid **and** rid<u>e</u>

Choose from:

a	e	i	o	u

1. c _ t **and** c _ te
2. m _ t **and** m _ te
3. p _ n **and** p _ ne
4. h _ p **and** h _ pe
5. c _ r **and** c _ re
6. f _ n **and** f _ ne

Adding le

Add <u>le</u> to make a word. Then
copy each word out. Can you
find six of the words in the
yellow box?

b i c y c _ _   _____

t a b _ _   _____

n e e d _ _   _____

c a n d _ _   _____

b e e t _ _   _____

bott_ _ _____

jung_ _ _____

kett_ _ _____

a	t	a	b	l	e	c
k	n	q	e	i	f	k
e	n	e	e	d	l	e
b	o	t	t	l	e	t
o	s	d	l	m	g	t
h	j	p	e	r	w	l
b	i	c	y	c	l	e

Adding ing

Make six new words by adding
<u>ing</u> to these letters. Then write
each word in a sentence.

k_ _ _   sw_ _ _

sl_ _ _   w_ _ _

str_ _ _   r_ _ _

1. _____

   _____

2. _____

   _____

3. _____

   _____

4. _____

   _____

5. _____

   _____

6. _____

   _____

More than one

Copy these words into the
right boxes.

mouse	book	house
fox	cow	tooth
foxes	houses	cows
books	mice	teeth

One	More than one
mouse	mice
tooth	teeth

Copy these words into the right boxes.

lambs	child	boxes
lamb	glove	babies
children	gloves	box
cherry	baby	cherries

One	More than one
box	boxes
glove	gloves

Present and past

The present is something we are doing now. The past is something we have already done.

Present – I am painting a picture.

Past – I have painted a picture.

Add <u>ing</u> for the present and <u>ed</u> for the past.

Present	Past
wait _ _ _	wait _ _
jump _ _ _	jump _ _

Present	Past
sail _ _ _	sail _ _
walk _ _ _	walk _ _
talk _ _ _	talk _ _
crawl _ _ _	crawl _ _
climb _ _ _	climb _ _
wash _ _ _	wash _ _
brush _ _ _	brush _ _
laugh _ _ _	laugh _ _
cook _ _ _	cook _ _

Present and past

Here are some more words in the present and in the past, but these are much trickier. They don't follow the usual rules. You will have to learn them by heart.

Present	Past
swimming	swam
sleeping	slept
singing	sang
running	ran
crying	cried
drawing	drew
eating	ate
reading	read

COVER UP the word lists on the
opposite page.
WRITE the missing words in the
lists below.
CHECK if you are right!

Present	Past
swimming	_ _ _ _
sleeping	_ _ _ _ _ _
_ _ _ _ _ _ _	sang
running	_ _ _
_ _ _ _ _ _	cried
_ _ _ _ _ _ _	drew
eating	_ _ _
reading	_ _ _ _

Tricky words

Some words are tricky to spell because they don't follow normal spelling patterns. Here are some of them.

 anchor

 biscuit

 chef

 saucer

 penguin

 pyjamas

 whistle

Copy out any of these words you find hard to spell. Cover them up, then write them from memory. Keep going until you know the spelling.

_____

_____

_____

_____

Say what is in each picture.
Spell the word next to it.

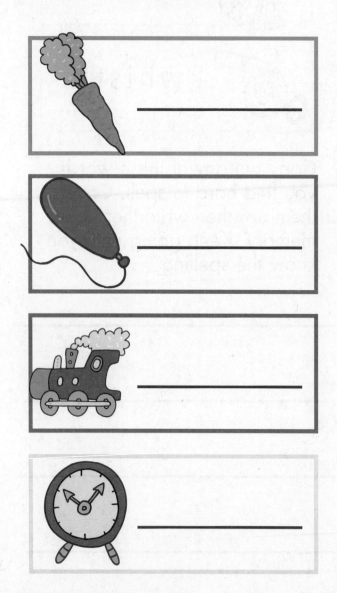

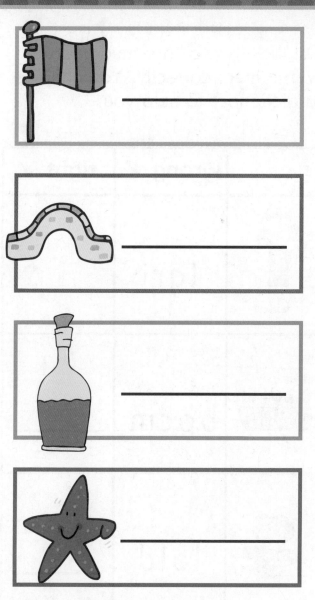

_____

_____

_____

_____

Now you can check your
answers at the back of
the book!

All these words are muddled up.
Write them correctly. You can use
a dictionary to help you.

	wrong ✗	right ✓
	lgri	_____
	bocm	_____
	lold	_____

	wrong ✗	right ✓
	ekti	_____
	rodo	_____
	rhia	_____
	rumd	_____
	ambl	_____
	cukd	_____

Right spellings

Choose the right word and put a tick in the box beside it.

1. Part of the foot.

toe	
tow	

2. A kind of fruit.

bury	
berry	

3. A very large sea animal.

wail	
whale	

4. To listen to a sound.

here	
hear	

5. Not old.

new	
knew	

6. Not strong.

week	
weak	

Now write the word.

1. _____

2. _____

3. _____

4. _____

5. _____

6. _____

Answers

Pages 8–9 Writing names

1. Sarah 2. Jack 3. Eva 4. Tom 5. Lily 6. Josh

Pages 10–11 First letter sounds

egg ant cap dog goat hen box fish
1. ant 2. box 3. cap 4. dog 5. egg 6. fish 7. goat 8. hen

Pages 12–13 First letters l to r

The king and queen had lots of pets.

They had a lion, and a monkey and a pig.

They had an owl in a nest.

They had a rabbit with big ears.

They fed them all on jelly and ice-cream.

ice-cream, jelly, king, lion, monkey, nest, owl, pig, queen, rabbit

Pages 14–15 First letter sounds

tap van wasp yellow zip
umbrella x-ray sun
1. sun 2. tap 3. umbrella 4. van
5. wasp 6. x-ray 7. yellow 8. zip

Pages 16–17 Animal alphabet

camel   horse   fox   dragon

goat   ape   bear   elephant

1. ape 2. bear 3. camel 4. dragon
5. elephant 6. fox 7. goat 8. horse

Pages 18–19 Food alphabet

ice-cream   milk   jam   pizza   orange   lemon

1. ice-cream 2. jam 3. lemon 4. milk 5. orange 6. pizza

Pages 20–21 w words

1. What time is it?
2. Where are you going?
3. Who is your best friend?

4. <u>When</u> is your birthday?
5. <u>Why</u> are you sad?
6. <u>Was</u> it a good game?

Pages 22–23 Short vowel 'a'

c<u>a</u>t   b<u>a</u>t   r<u>a</u>t   h<u>a</u>t   1. bag 2. dad 3. map 4. fat

Pages 24–25 Short vowel 'e'

w<u>e</u>b   n<u>e</u>t   b<u>e</u>d   r<u>e</u>d   1. ten 2. fed 3. pen 4. wet

Pages 26–27 short vowel 'i'

p<u>i</u>g   s<u>i</u>x   w<u>i</u>g   p<u>i</u>n   1. dig 2. lick 3. big 4. did

Pages 28–29 Short vowel 'o'

d<u>o</u>g   f<u>o</u>x   m<u>o</u>p   l<u>o</u>g   1. got 2. on 3. top 4. hot

Pages 30–31 Short vowel 'u'

b<u>u</u>s   c<u>u</u>p   d<u>u</u>ck   s<u>u</u>n   1. run 2. hug 3. mum 4. mud

Pages 32–33 Second chance

d<u>o</u>g, c<u>u</u>p, p<u>i</u>g, b<u>a</u>t, b<u>e</u>d, w<u>i</u>g, c<u>a</u>t, f<u>o</u>x, w<u>e</u>b, d<u>u</u>ck, n<u>e</u>t, s<u>u</u>n, r<u>a</u>t, b<u>u</u>s

Pages 34–35 Three-letter words

deb = bed, ibb = bib, gge = egg, tca = cat, oyb = boy, acr = car, ebe = bee, ubs = bus, tab = bat

Pages 36–37 ch sound

<u>ch</u>air, <u>ch</u>ick, <u>ch</u>erry, <u>ch</u>ildren, <u>ch</u>ocolate, <u>ch</u>eese, <u>ch</u>ur<u>ch</u>

Pages 38–39 Look carefully

hutch: watch/switch/witch   sack: brick/sock/duck

Answers

Pages 40–41 Wordsearch for sh

```
s h a r k n b
h m f o d e r
e d i s h s u
e h s r u l s
p s h e d o h
```

shark brush shed sheep

dish fish

Pages 42–43 br sound

<u>br</u>ain, <u>br</u>anch, <u>br</u>oom, <u>br</u>idle, <u>br</u>ook, <u>br</u>ing, <u>br</u>im, <u>br</u>eeze, <u>br</u>onze, <u>br</u>ave

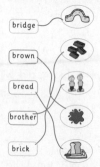

bridge

brown

bread

brother

brick

Pages 44–45 cr sound

<u>cr</u>y, <u>cr</u>ash, <u>cr</u>ew, <u>cr</u>isp, <u>cr</u>umb, <u>cr</u>unch, <u>cr</u>eak, <u>cr</u>eam, <u>cr</u>ate, <u>cr</u>ocodile

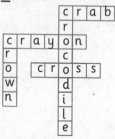

```
      c r a b
      r
c r a y o n
r     c
o   c r o s s
w     d
n     i
      l
      e
```

Pages 46–47 dr or tr

<u>dr</u>um, <u>dr</u>ink, <u>tr</u>actor, <u>dr</u>agon, <u>tr</u>iangle, <u>tr</u>uck
1. dragon 2. drum 3. drink 4. tractor

Pages 48–49 Sounds: st str sp sl sw

<u>st</u>ar, <u>sp</u>oon, <u>st</u>amp, <u>sw</u>ing, <u>str</u>awberry, <u>sl</u>ide

Pages 50–51 Wordsearch for bl cl fl

c	l	c	b	l	u	e
l	f	l	b	l	f	e
f	l	o	w	e	r	s
l	a	c	l	o	u	d
g	g	k	c	h	l	b
z	b	k	b	b	l	l
y	l	b	l	a	c	k

blue
cloud
flowers
clock
flag
black

Pages 52–53 th sound

thumb, throne, three, thistle, bath, toothbrush, maths

Pages 54–55 Double letters: ll

bell, wall, ball, jelly, umbrella, roller skate, yellow, balloons, caterpillars

Pages 56–57 Double letters: dd rr tt ss zz

bottle, kettle, teddy, cherry, ladder, carrot, pizza, grass, butterfly

Pages 58–59 Double letters: oo

book, moon, igloo, spoon, balloon, kangaroo, door, tooth, hook

Pages 60–61 ow or ou?

cow, clown, mouse, house, owl, flowers, rainbow, crown, window

Pages 62–63 Middle sound: oa and ea

1. I felt sea sick on the boat.
2. I saw a goat on the farm.
3. I put on my coat.
4. I can eat a pear.
5. I found a feather.

Pages 64–65 Middle sound: ai

rain, train, trainer, paint, hair, rainbow

Answers

Pages 66–67 ee or ea

ee	ea
cheese	ice-cream
queen	leaf
wheel	
tree	

Pages 68–69 Different middles ai ae

seat, train, beak, tail, beads, rain

Pages 70–71 Silent letters

knife/guitar/knight/wheel/comb/thumb/wrist/badge/
gnome/knitting

Pages 72–73 Rhyming words

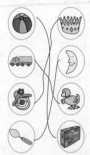

Incy Wincy Spider climbed up
the water spout.

Down came the rain and washed
the spider out.

Out came the sunshine and dried
up all the rain.

Now Incy Wincy Spider climbed
up the spout again!

Pages 74–75 Same sounds

tie/fly, rain/plane, four/saw, gnome/comb

Pages 76–77 Word syllables

Possible answers are: el-e-phant, tel-e-phone,
mag-i-cian, pol-ice-woman, ba-na-na, but-ter-fly

Pages 78–79 Breaking down words

cl-oud, fl-ow-er, ch-ur-ch, cr-ow-n, sp-i-der

Pages 80–81 Everyday words

1. would 2. because 3. laugh 4. once 5. water 6. Here

Pages 84–85 Days of the week

On <u>Monday</u> I go swimming.
On <u>Tuesday</u> I play football.
On <u>Wednesday</u> I feed the ducks.
On <u>Thursday</u> I help Dad do the shopping.
On <u>Friday</u> I go to see my gran.
On <u>Saturday</u> I go to a party.
On <u>Sunday</u> I help Mum wash her car.

Pages 86–87 Compound words

star+fish = starfish, butter+fly = butterfly,
cow+boy = cowboy, horse+shoe = horseshoe
rain+bow = rainbow

Pages 88–89 Compound words

pig+tail = pigtail, jelly+fish = jellyfish,
hair+brush = hairbrush, drum+stick = drumstick

Pages 90–91 Patterns in words

ick
est
ate
tle
ight
ing

Pages 92–93 Hidden words

You can find more than one little word in some big words.
1. ball, all, on 2. up 3. some, thing, met, in, thin, so, me
4. the, her, moth, he 5. or 6. ten, kit, it 7. in, din, no 8. win, in

Pages 94–95 Definitions

butterfly   panda   sock   banana   frog   brush

Pages 100–101 Magic e

cap–cape, hat–hate, her–here, bit–bite, not–note, tub–tube

1. cut and cute 2. mat and mate 3. pin and pine
4. hop and hope 5. car and care 6. fin and fine

Answers

Pages 102–103 Adding le

bicy<u>cle</u>, ta<u>ble</u>, need<u>le</u>, cand<u>le</u>, beet<u>le</u>, bot<u>tle</u>, jun<u>gle</u>, ket<u>tle</u>

Pages 104–105 Adding ing

<u>king</u>, swi<u>ng</u>, sli<u>ng</u>, wi<u>ng</u>, stri<u>ng</u>, ri<u>ng</u>

Pages 106–107 More than one

One: mouse/book/house/fox/cow/tooth
More than one: mice/books/houses/foxes/cows/teeth

Pages 108–109 More than one

One: box/glove/lamb/child/baby/cherry
More than one: boxes/gloves/lambs/children/babies/cherries

Pages 110–111 Present and past

<u>Present</u>	<u>Past</u>
wait<u>ing</u>	wait<u>ed</u>
jump<u>ing</u>	jump<u>ed</u>
sail<u>ing</u>	sail<u>ed</u>
walk<u>ing</u>	walk<u>ed</u>
talk<u>ing</u>	talk<u>ed</u>
crawl<u>ing</u>	crawl<u>ed</u>
climb<u>ing</u>	climb<u>ed</u>
wash<u>ing</u>	wash<u>ed</u>
brush<u>ing</u>	brush<u>ed</u>
laugh<u>ing</u>	laugh<u>ed</u>
cook<u>ing</u>	cook<u>ed</u>

Pages 116–117 Test your spelling

carrot, balloon, train, clock, flag, bridge, bottle, starfish

Pages 118–119 Right spellings

lgri = girl, bocm = comb, lold = doll, ekti = kite, rodo = door,
rhia = hair, rumd = drum, ambl = lamb, cukd = duck

Pages 120–121 Right spellings

1. toe 2. berry 3. whale 4. hear 5. new 6. weak